Mrs Weber's Diary

27 March 82

To Margaret.

With all best wishes
for your new job. Come
back & see us soon!

Tatty
xx

Also by Posy Simmonds
TRUE LOVE

Posy Simmonds

Mrs Weber's Diary

JONATHAN CAPE   THIRTY BEDFORD SQUARE   LONDON

The Characters

1	**Edmund HEEP**	(father & whisky salesman)
2	**Jolyon HEEP**	(at secondary school)
3	**Jo HEEP**	(mother & tennis coach)
4	**Julian HEEP**	(at secondary school, founder of 'The Snotty Throttlers' pop group)
5	**Benji WEBER**	(at nursery school)
6	**George WEBER**	(father, Senior Lecturer in Liberal Studies at a polytechnic)
7	**Wendy WEBER**	(mother, ex-nurse, now writer of children's books)
8	**Pussy**	(Weber cat, neutered tom)
9	**Amanda WEBER**	
10	**Tamsin WEBER**	(twins, at primary school)
11	**Sophie WEBER**	(at secondary school)
12	**Beverley WEBER**	(at secondary school)
13	**Belinda WEBER**	(at secondary school, taking 2 'A' Levels)
14	**Stanhope WRIGHT**	(father, creative director of Beazeley & Buffin Advertising)
15	**Trish WRIGHT**	(mother, former art gallery assistant, Stanhope's 2nd wife)
16	**Willy WRIGHT**	
17	**Jocasta WRIGHT**	(art student, Stanhope's daughter from his 1st marriage)

January

Friday   Colinshawes' Party   8.30   (Babysitter)

Saturday   Woke late with ~~the~~ frightful hangover. Broke New Year resolution.
   (George - very smug, kept his, which is to Get Up and Grab the Day
   by the Balls.)
   X (Pay Milkman)
   Asprin
   veg.
Listened to ^radio programme about ~~mutig mat~~ mutagens damaging DNA in cells & giving
us all cancer. Kids went to local panto in Assembly Rooms.

$$\begin{array}{r} £52 \\ \times 32 \\ \hline 104 \\ 1560 \\ \hline £1,664 \end{array}$$

Sunday.   Woke early. Pot Roast, but overdid the ~~fin~~ fines herbes.
   After lunch, drove to Fladgewell Downs with the Wrights & the Heeps.
   Girls stayed at home.

Tues. Washed druggets in the bath this morning. Removed ground-in chewing gum with carbon tetrachloride.
One guinea pig (Derek) very poorly with husky cough – not long for this world I think. Benji very INTERESTED, so thought it a good time to explain DEATH.

Wednesday. George's DAY OFF.

Spent day finishing children's story ready for publishers to see on Fri.

Poor Derek shuffled off mortal coil. George explained death again to Benji. I think it was the musty HAY myself. Disinfected hutch with Lysol. Twins to BROWNIES.

Thurs. Waste cabbage leaves from grocer for guinea pigs RABBIT PELLETS
✓ Ring VET. Bran?
✓ Bank Finish Book.

Fri. Appointment at publishers 11.00. Got early train to town – G dropped me at station.

As Wendy waits for a London train.....

QUICK! Get an AMBULANCE!

A very pregnant woman has gone into LABOUR! How lucky that Wendy was once a NURSE at St Thomas' Hospital....

CLEAR the WAITING ROOM! GET SOME SCISSORS!

THINKS: Thank God I've got LACES in my shoes!

Wendy delivers Mrs Pat Newby of a fine baby BOY in the waiting room, BEFORE the ambulance arrives!

After the event, Wendy is interviewed by the Evening Paper....

It was a very EASY labour.... I was a NURSE before I married, you see...

I used my SHOE LACES to tie the...

What does your HUSBAND do?

He's a Liberal Studies lecturer...and he's a house-husband...

...anyway, I wrapped the baby in a coat, to prevent HEAT LOSS...

You've got 6 children yourself, am I right?

I also WRITE children's books... in fact, I was on my way to see my publishers...

And HOW d'you feel, now?

Like a large GIN!

That evening, when Wendy gets home:

George! I'm ALL OVER the PAPER...I'm BLOODY FURIOUS! LOOK!

EVENING ECHO
EXPRESS DELIVERY FOR MOTHER OF SIX!

XPRESS DELIVERY OR MOTHER OF SIX!

Oh mother! It's quicker by rail! The bundle arriving at Platform 4 was an express delivery for Mrs Patricia Newby (23)...a baby boy, born 2 weeks prematurely, at the Main Line Station this morning.

It seems Baby tired of waiting in the waiting room and signalled his arr-

and attractive mother of 6, Wendy Webber, calmed Pat during the delivery. "I've had six," said Wendy, "so I should know a bit about it!"

Shopping spree
Wendy, (36), who likes to read children's books as a hobby, is married to an arts teacher. She was on a shopping spree to

It makes my blood BOIL! This endless CONDESCENSION to WOMEN!.... BIRTH as a JOKE!

NO mention of my being a trained NURSE! 'Off on a SHOPPING SPREE!' MY GOD! HONESTLY!!

NO mention of how I used my SHOE LACES!

NO mention of my initiative & common sense!

Yes, & I'm NOT an ARTS teacher...I'm a Senior Lecturer in Further Education

As a matter of interest, WHAT did you DO with your SHOE LACES?

Because of that paper's TRIVIALISING attitude to women, YOU & General Public will NEVER know how my laces helped at the BIRTH of a HUMAN BEING!

January

Wednesday — George late lecture.

Thurs. HEADLICE at Benji's school. Told Mrs Pye it's NOTHING to be ashamed of.
Still FURIOUS with that frightful RACIST Sara Nutting. I wouldn't speak
to her ~~at~~ at ALL if she weren't so good at community fund raising.

Outside the nursery school, consternation reigns:

January

Ring Lydia / Ma / Plumber

Mr Harris?   256094

Children's Xmas Thank you letters

G to inspect ROOF.

February

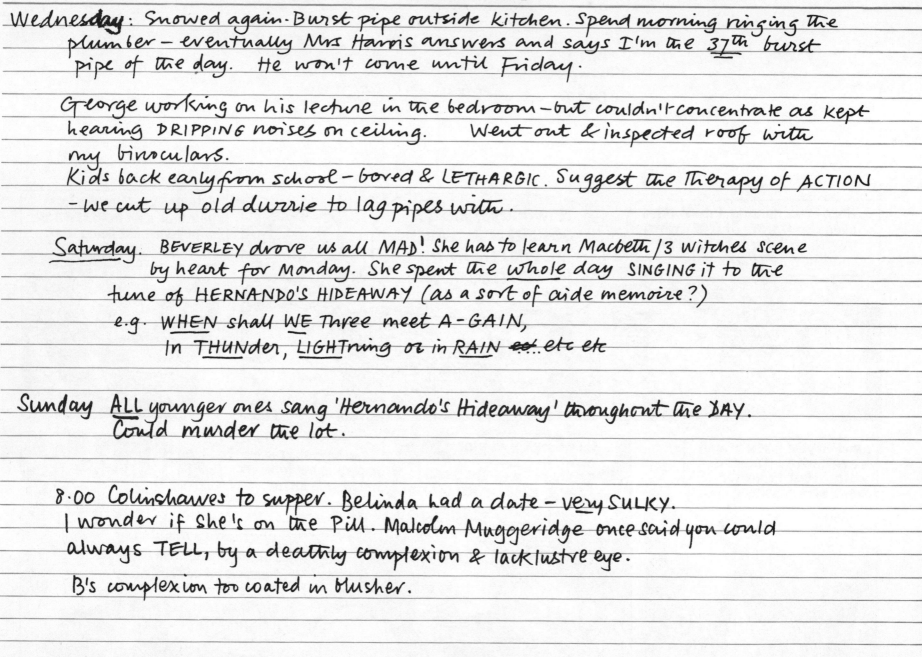

Wednesday: Snowed again. Burst pipe outside kitchen. Spend morning ringing the plumber — eventually Mrs Harris answers and says I'm the 37th burst pipe of the day. He won't come until Friday.

George working on his lecture in the bedroom — but couldn't concentrate as kept hearing DRIPPING noises on ceiling.   Went out & inspected roof with my binoculars.

Kids back early from school — bored & LETHARGIC. Suggest the Therapy of ACTION — we cut up old durrie to lag pipes with.

Saturday. BEVERLEY drove us all MAD! She has to learn Macbeth/3 Witches scene by heart for Monday. She spent the whole day SINGING it to the tune of HERNANDO'S HIDEAWAY (as a sort of aide memoire?)

e.g. WHEN shall WE three meet A-GAIN,
  In THUNder, LIGHTning or in RAIN etc..etc etc

Sunday ALL younger ones sang 'Hernando's Hideaway' throughout the DAY. Could murder the lot.

8.00 Colinshawes to supper. Belinda had a date — very SULKY.
I wonder if she's on the Pill. Malcolm Muggeridge once said you could always TELL, by a deathly complexion & lacklustre eye.

B's complexion too coated in blusher.

My parents really are **PEASANTS!**

They look so **SCRUFFY & UNKEMPT**...they **NEVER** buy things that **LAST**...

Belinda's reverie is interrupted by her boyfriend's arrival....

Mum, Dad...this is Johnny Macniece

Hi! Have some home-made **PLONK!**

er...**NO thanks** awfully.

SILKEN EYES *Françoise Sagan*

Typical! They're always pressing **ALCOHOL** on you

Off you go, kids, & have a **BALL!**

So that's your little homestead, Belinda. Most **QUAINT!**

Not for long! I'm getting out, when I leave school!

This area used to be really O.K. till my parents' lot turned it into an **URBAN VILLAGE**

I'm **SICK** of lentils, old denim, Batik prints ...my parents' obsession with **SEX**..& their endless rapping about the boring old **SIXTIES**....

...when **DAD** joined student sit ins & Mum was a **FLOWER CHILD & EARTH-MOTHER**...

Eldridge Cleave SOUL ON ICE

My parents are **SO IRRESPONSIBLE** - they don't care **WHO** I go out with..**WHERE I go**...they don't care about my school work

..They don't care about **ANYTHING!**

Same with mine - they think the world owes them a living.

*Meanwhile, at **HOME**:*

Belinda really should be working for her **A Levels**.

But we don't believe in **forcing** her to stay in... she must learn to make her own **discipline**...

And we never pry into her private life...we're **NOT SPIES**...we trust her, don't we, George?

We don't want her to have any of the **HANG-UPS** we had about **WORK & SEX**...

When I **THINK** of how **MY** parents were! "Your **HAIR!** Those awful **CLOTHES!** You think the world owes you a living ...!"

Gosh yes! I had to face **INQUISITIONS!**

"Where've you been? What did you do? Who did you meet?"

Belinda just doesn't know what she's missing!

February

Blind Kit
Stiffener
UHU glue

3lbs mince

170 ~~170~~ ~~1270~~ 14'
170

Drop 170 cms
+ 12"

4 metres

170 cms

March

Tuesday Jocasta W. came over with some illustrations for my book.
Thought she'd rather OVERDONE the atmosphere of the high rise estate
— a bit squalid. But she'd drawn SAL very well — & SAL's MUM. Hope
Walmer & Willox like them. Strange that Belinda's friendly with Jocasta —
they're both so different. B. thinks of nothing but her appearance & MEN.

March

Jocasta couldn't care less about either

I suppose J is useful for buying drinks in the Pub — also she's plain & doesn't present any competition.

March

Ring Walmer & Wilcox re Jocasta's drawings

Weds Jennifer Cole } 4·00 (Mavis school run)
Vernon Twiss }

(veg soup?)

This is a meeting at **WALMER & WILCOX** to discuss Wendy's book and Jocasta's illustrations: Present are **VERNON TWISS** (*Art Director*), **ALISTAIR GRANT** (*Sales Director*), **JENNIFER COLE** (*Children's Editor*), **MAX FURNEAUX** (*Editorial Director*), **SUE COMYNGE-KERR** (*secretary*), **BILL BEACON** (*Production Manager*), & Young **WILCOX**, Chairman's nephew (*Book Club Rights*) .....

"It's dead boring waiting for Mum to get back from work", said Sal.

"I'm starving. I want me tea. I'll go and play in the 'lifts'."

7

This is **JUST** what we should be doing now. It's **DIFFERENT** & it's **REALISTIC**... the vast majority of children see **NO** reflection of themselves or the world they live in, in the books they're given to read

Yes! The drawings are really ...er.. aren't they, don't you think? That touch of **OTTO DIX, NEO SUPER-REALISM**.. ...**GROSZ**...

THAT'S just what **I** think...they're **GROSS**, ugly...a **CONDESCENDING** view of the **LESS** fortunate by a middle class writer...

I always say to them: Write what you **KNOW** about....

It's not on! I can't give **STUFF** like **THIS** to the reps! **IMAGINE** old Tom trying to flog this to **HATCHARDS**!

And the art work doesn't exploit the cheap **4** colour repro deal we've made with the **POLISH** printers, now the **zloty's** stable

Ted Evans 230478

Ring Garage
Engine misfiring when idling
perhaps a air leak carburettor?
 CHECK inlet manifold. Slow running jet.

	Chicken Pox	Measles	G. Measles	Mumps
Belinda	✓	?	✓	✓
Beverley	✓	✓	✓	X ?
Sophie	✓	—	✓	✗ ✓ ?
Amanda	?	—	✓	✗ ✓ ?
Tamsin	✓	—	?	✓
Benji	—	—	—	✓

April

Wednesday — My turn school run. Trish rings — very depressed — says she's had a TOTAL PERSONALITY TRANSPLANT since Willy was born & can't cope.... spends most of day in dressing gown, tipping back VALIUM, trying to keep Willy & that enormous house clean. Promise to go round tomorrow & cheer her up. She says marvellous, as only person she sees otherwise is ADRIAN & we all know about him.

This is Adrian Smythe, ex-journalist, now a house-husband, and his daughters, Amy & Saffron....

Now Amy's **2**, Moira's gone back to full-time work at the Beeb.

Amy

Saffron

Moira & I have completely reversed **RÔLES**... now I stay at **HOME** with the children & write my book in the evenings....

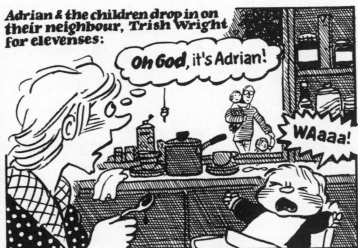

Adrian & the children drop in on their neighbour, Trish Wright for elevenses:

Oh God, it's Adrian!

WAaaa!

Excuse the **mess**, Adrian.... I got off to rather a late start today...

werr!

Honestly, Trish, don't worry! I know **all** about **MESS** now! I never realised before just how **time-consuming** housework **is**!

Don't you **HATE** doing **FLOORS**? I do. I have to do mine **EVERY** day to stop the **GROT** building up.

You know, people don't realise that housekeeping's a **REAL** job....

I must say, I find the chores **tough going**... I tend to get up very **EARLY** & get the **whole lot** done before **breakfast**... that way I've got the rest of the day for the **KIDS**....

I hate saying "DADDY'S BUSY" all the time.

April

Poor Trish... of course having 1st baby at **36** & abandoning career are quite a shock NEITHER Stanhope NOR Jocasta do a damn thing in the house & Trish won't employ a daily any more as she thinks it's wrong. Wonder what Jocasta's like as a stepdaughter? T. says they get on better now – says Jocasta's got v. interested in GRAPH THEORY & sees some Cambridge Maths Professor.

And we've been having **SUCH** fun! Tell Trish what you've grown in your little garden, Saffron.

Tomatoes

Well, we **WILL** have super **tomatoes** in the summer, darling... but you've just grown some lovely **chervil**...eh?

'es

Ooh Amy! That's a *lovely BEETLE!* And you found it in Trish's utility room...shall we take it home for your *NATURE TABLE?*

And how's **Willy?** Ooh, he's a bit *soggy*...d'you want him changed, Trish?

No thanks

You know, I'm going to miss all this when I go back to **WORK**.

I see...how's the book? What's it called **now?**

"*The Self-Fettered Super Char*"

Or: "*One Woman's Sink is another Man's Swimming Pool.*" **GRRR!**

April

10 Monday

Golf

11 Tuesday

Lunch Simpsons 1·30
Lyric Theatre tickets

12 Wednesday

Henry Portam Lunch
The Grange 1·00

13 Thursday

Le Gavroche

14 Friday

Carol · Chez Hubert 8·30

15 Saturday

Golf.
Willis, Cooper, Keighley

16 Sunday

Golf
Grooches · Drinks 6·00·

Staff meeting 10

Tutorial - Steve Tripp 2.00

Tutorial - Amanda Khan 4.00

15

Wendy's turn to cook.

16

My turn to cook.

April

Friday : My birthday. Children brought in breakfast tray. Nearly wept : Clay mice (made at school) from TWINS, BIRFday card from Benji & guinea pigs, hankies from Sophie & Bev. & frightfully expensive scent (Yves St Laurent) from Belinda. Lovely freesias & a WOK from George. WOK came with Chinese cook book & 6 prs chopsticks. All sang Happy Birthday round the bed. So sweet. George's Ma even sent card. Mine sent v. generous book token.   After nursery school, picked Benji up & went round to Diane's...

April

May

Sunday: Took children to TATE Gallery. George encouraged Benji to touch all the sculptures & then had a long ~~argument~~ discussion with attendant about what G. calls "Haptic Experience".

Tues. Street party Committee Meeting 3.00

✓ Sara N.   Adrian ✓
✓ Trish   Pippa ?
✓ Emily   Mrs Pope ?

Weds }
Thurs } G's turn School Run / Cooking.

 Fri G. working at Home.   P.T.A Meeting?

Besides lecturing in Liberal Studies, GEORGE WEBER also WRITES. On fine evenings, he does this in his garden:

The Weis-Megalith: A structuralist Interpretation of the career of Buckminster Fuller.

ROGER TIMMIS, George's neighbour, READS. He does this in HIS garden.

FUMBLE

Sometimes, husky Roger scrambles over the stout wall dividing the 2 gardens.....

Take a gander at THIS, Georgie... bit of ORIGHT... WOOrRR!

Well... not really my cup of tea, Roger.

No...now I come to think about it...she's **NOT** your cup of tea...little, bookish chap like you...big girl like her..... she'd want a **REAL** man!

Only kidding, George. Have some beer.

Look, Roger, I am trying to **WRITE** a **CRUCIAL ESSAY**....

NO BEER? *That* won't make you grow into a big strong boy! All right!.....off I go... ...here's lead in your pencil, Georgie!

!☆☆�!!

Was that **TIMMIS** & his girly magazines **AGAIN?**

YES! A most **OFFENSIVE, SEXIST** periodical! He also made **INSINUATIONS** about my....

Oh, ignore him...those magazines are his **HOMEWORK**.... I always say *Those that can, DO*...and *those that can't, STUDY*

Look, I forgot, **THIS** arrived for you from Canada.

Oh **NO!** It's my manuscript! * McGill have turned it down!

* The manuscript is George's collection of critical essays, entitled "Weimar, Chicago, & the Cultural Squash Ball," featuring Moholy-Nagy, Charles Morris & Marshall McLuhan.

Listen, the reader says "Regretfully, the full complexity of your interesting arguments would be obscured by the heavy editing needed to bring the book down to manageable proportions.

?

Manageable Proportions! FOOL! Canada's **full** of **trees** to make into **paper!**

IDIOTS! CRETINS! Can't they understand the need for us pioneer academic anatomists? 5 years of my life **WASTED!**

Don't *taunt* him, Roger...he's had a disappointment.

In his anguish, George performs an act of Brute strength upon 600 pages of manuscript....

GRUNT!

Rrip!

Wendy & Roger go into BOGGLE OVER-DRIVE:

Bloody hell! I must get back to my **BULLWORKER!**

He could have **RUPTURED** himself!

My work isn't lost to **POSTERITY**, friends... I've got 4 copies at the **POLY.**

May

Monday

Start planning food for Street Party. Trish lends me book on
Cuisine Minceur — very healthy concept, everything low cholesterol: lobster,
truffles, foie gras etc. Très economical.   Anyway, I'm getting on
splendidly with my WOK.

Spend afternoon squishing up veg. in Mouligrater & make
1 doz spinach QUICHES. Shoved the lot in the freezer.

Belinda babysat. G & I went to cinema — Les Enfants du Paradis,
for the nth time.

Wednesday.

Terribly worried about Sophie's reading — her spelling appalling too.
Met Pippa who said she can't understand why George & I bother
with comprehensives — She's got Rufus, Alice & Josh down for private schools.
(George is fed up with what he calls 'her weary, elitist lament')

Beverley has to learn chunk of "The Ancient Mariner." Luckily, she can't
sing it to 'Hernando's Hideaway' — doesn't fit, thank God.

Actually, I had a go in the bath & discovered you CAN sing
'The Ancient Mariner' to 'It happened in Monterey'!

Thurs

Working in library. George collecting Benji nursery school.
my turn CAR

Mrs Platt
763070
MRS PLAT-

Here is George taking Benji home from nursery school on the bus:

What an engaging child Benji is! How the ladies love him!

I drawed a pussy-cat today!

Aaah! How sweet!

My name's Benji.

Daddy, that lady's got *BIG BOOZIES*... *why's* that lady got big *BOOZIES*?

Look at that great big road digger, Benji!

Why has she got...

WHY has that lady got big *BOOZUMS*!?

Now look, Benji...all ladies have bosoms & men don't. Now stop shouting.

⸝THINKS⸝ This is interesting...Benji bestows on me, as FATHER, the charismatic & sacramental prestige of the PRIEST...we can see the passengers of this bus as a CON-GREGATION taking part in the mediation between TABOO and SOCIAL RATIONALITY....

They're assisting at a *unique* moment in the *restructuring* of Benji's conceptual growth..diachron-ically...synchron-ically.....

But Benji has other thoughts:

THAT lady hasn't got *ANY BOOZUMS!* *WHY* hasn't that lady got....?

Look, I'm sorry if my child *embarrasses* you.. he's coming to terms with *TABOO*...

Of course, in ADULTS, I would *DEPLORE* such *CHAUVINISTIC* behaviour...but HE is at a stage when differences between MEN & WOMEN are very ..er..*SIGNIFICANT*...

Why hasn't she.....

Time we got off, Benji.

Why?

Must be a CRANK

And the way you all **PATRONISED** the people from **Alma Street & Balaclava Terrace!**

Mind you, I'll be surprised if they turn up this year...the middle class have driven them out...

I know **JUST** what it's going to be like...like a painting by **PIETER BRUEGHEL** the **ELDER**....

Last year it was **SUPER**.. we met **ALL** the **LOCALS.**

Hallo, darlings

Now, only a little **MEAD,** Sasha!

Where are they this year?

You **KNOW** I hate **OLIVES** Mummy

Drinking **SPIRITS** up the other end

Wendy! You **DIDN'T** make **ALL** those!

Yes, I did.....but **QUICHES** are **MARVELLOUS!** They're all out of my freezer. **NOW,** the vegetarian ones are at the front.

PIZZA too! How **SUPER!**

Whole meal flour makes lovely pastry

NEVER AGAIN!

It's Marks & Sparks' **PLONK.** O.K. isn't it?

Daddy, Rollo's nicked my **COKE!**

Shall we join the **PEASANTS?**

· P. SIMMONDS ·

June

Friday.

    Went round to Trish's for tea. She was glued to Wimbledon. Seemed much better — said she was off Valium, said Stanhope was well & Willy was well. & Jocasta was.... Jocasta was having an AFFAIR — it appears with Stefan Torte, Carduelian Professor of Maths at Cambridge — Fellow of Judas College. Who'd have thought it — he's got children Jocasta's age!

    Apparently he lives up the road from Trish & it all began when Jocasta went to see him about her graph theory — he's now helping her with Catastrophe Theory ... & other things besides.

Still feel rather badly over Jocasta's illustrations that W&W turned down (though do now think the artist they used is more suitable.)
Anyway, J. came in with her end of term project for art ~~st~~ school — she'd done an AD for MOTHERHOOD.

Join the Professionals:

The country needs volunteer (or willing conscript) **mothers** in the 18-28 age bracket, although there is an upper age limit of 35 for special abilities.

Motherhood.
A mother provides a **vital service** to the country, which often goes **unrecognised** and **unrewarded**. Motherhood costs spare time and the chance of travel. But it does bring much in return: the chance to develop skills & resourcefulness. Above all, it is a **challenge** and a chance to **serve** the country in a worthwhile way.

Raw material.
You may think we ask an awful lot of a young mother. But we aren't asking the impossible. All that is needed is the right raw material and the right training, during which, those selected often think they are going through **hell**.

Isolation.
The training is straightforward: the Health Visitor, the District Nurse, the Social Worker & the Media have to show the mother they can do everything the mother can do. Only better.

Combat.
Today's young mothers have got a **job** to do, whether it's holding the fort single handed, being in the thick of action in a playgroup or fighting dangerous household germs.

God bless them.
Men are eligible to join the **Mothers** too. Although they are not called upon for active service, they provide a useful backup team for the **breeding woman.** During her short service commission, a Mother is assured of a warm, patronising interest from the **Inland Revenue, the D.H.S.S. & Advertising Agencies.**

It's a good life in the Mothers and it's a **REAL job too.**

THE MOTHERS.

I think I may be one of the women you're looking for.
Name _____
Address _____
_____ Date of birth _____
Please send me a brochure & full information.
To: Mothers' Application Centre

July

Monday. Letter from Kevin about our summer hols in Tresoddit. Says we can stay
2 or 3 weeks in Aug, provided 2 of us don't mind sleeping in little
room above old gutting shed.   Very keen for us to see his EDIBLE LANDSCAPE —
— cabbage, lettuce, sweet corn, beans as far as eye can see — & ALL ORGANIC.

Tues.   Most of Girls' school mates seem to be going to Majorca or
Yugoslavia for their hols. Don't know HOW their parents can
AFFORD it — esp. some of those families on The Collingwood Estate.
Sophie says the Wheelers going to CRETE.
However, Girls don't seem to feel deprived. Asked them if they
minded not going abroad & Sophie & Bev broke into song thus:—
    "We'd rather stay in Reading in the rain
        You can stick your España!" (tune of Viva España)
Extraordinary. Where did they learn that?

Thursday. Prepare for Frisbee's visit — arrives Heathrow tomorrow.
    George says Frisbee's applied for a research-linked studentship
at the poly. Apparently, he's still into ethno-botany.
    Moved Benji in with twins. Twins objected — can't be helped. No spare room.

July

Tuesday. FOUL weather – really cold for July. This morning George tripped over Benji's
    trike at bottom of stairs & hurt his knee. (Small contusion) Insisted on large piece of
plaster.   We had annual row about moving somewhere bigger. Then G. stumped
off to Summer Seminar at Poly, taking walking stick we use for blackberrying
– said he needed VISIBLE SIGN of being MAIMED.

Of Course I would like a bigger place – esp. a room of my own. There's nowhere in this
bloody house where I can write out of earshot of guinea pigs.

    Tamsin & Amanda TERRIFIED of visit to dentist on Thurs. Reassure them.
Rang Jo – she's still coaching tennis 4 days a week. Decide to invite her & Edmund to
dinner.

    They arrive early. Twins tell Edmund about impending dental visit. Edmund
undoes ALL my good work – terrifies girls with stories about 'the jolly old
IVORY CARPENTER' & his WHACKING GREAT DRILL.

George brings Andrew Wingate from Poly School of Architecture back for dinner.
Suspect Ulterior Motives.

July

Edmund rings (sounded like from pub phone.box) to thank us for 'a very genial evening'.
He DOES have nice manners, in his own way.   I ask after Jo — E. says Jo has
a big day's coaching at St Leonard's Inter-Schools Trophy tomorrow — so would
George & I care to step out for a quick noggin this evening? I decline — it's
so tricky with babysitters etc.

The appearance of genial Edmund HEEP (& friends), in the saloon bar of the *Castle & Ball*, causes concern amongst those with more *delicate fibres* to their natures:

For Edmund was born under a very RUDE sign.

Evening, **Squire!** How're you, **cod's eyes?**

NOT scrambling ALREADY, Squadron Leader?

Oh God!

There is *NO* limit to *EDMUND'S* generosity........ .double brandies *ALL ROUND*...!

Now, what about a spot of **BELLY TIMBER**? Bangers, anyone? **Scotch Egg?**

Actually, looks like **YOU'VE** been putting away **too many** of the jolly old **OEUFS ECOSSAIS**, Ernest... **look** at that **TUM TUM!**

What a **SHOWER!**

TUM TUM!! I'll have you know it's a **wall of steel..** ...solid **MUSCLE!**

What say I **PUNCH** it, then.. ...**HARD** as I can? Bet you a fiver you'll say **OEUF!!** Har Har Har !!!

Edmund soon has his companions in thrall:

I say, what's **brown & steaming &** comes out of **COWES backwards?**

The **Isle of Wight Ferry!** Har! Har!

And d'you know the difference between some **PYGMIES** & a **Ladies' Athletics** team?

Pygmies are...

July

But Squadron Leader 'Flapper' Noakes (rtd.), has had enough.....

> Look here, Heep, I don't care for this sort of *mucky* talk.

> Right you are, my old *Squabbling Bleeder*, ...sorry I spoke.

Whilst Edmund visits the little boys' room:

> I knew a chap in the **Forces** like **HEEP** – **FRIGHTFUL PAIN!** Y'know how we shut him up? Bet him a *fiver* he couldn't get **3 BILLIARD BALLS** in his **MOUTH** ....

> ...He got 'em **IN** but he couldn't get 'em **OUT!** Dentist had to do that! Ha Ha!

> Be a good chap, Ernest...go & get some balls from the **SNOOKER** table....

Thus Edmund undertakes a risky wager. His teeth are in peril.

> Right! £5, Edmund, if you get them **IN AND OUT!**

> IN!

> OUT!

> **HOW** did you **do** it, man!?

> Simple: I removed my **DENTURES** as well. I've always had a **big mouth**.

> Thank you, Flapper...in the words of the harlot: it's been a business doing pleasure with you!

Petrol
- ✓ Keys
- ✓ Cheque Bk
- ✓ Radio
- ✓ ~~Picnic~~ Picnic
- ✓ THERMOS

~~PHOTS~~
KWELLS

Empty frig
Water plants
Cat food
Taps
Electricity
Bthrm window

GARAGE
MILKMAN
PAPER STOP?

Phone George & Ma-
   " mine.

Watch
Camera
Address Bk ✓
Books ✓
Heavy Socks ✓
Wellies ✓
Bathers
Hair Dryer ✓

Benji's Teddy

And here is a **SON** of Tresoddit, **KEVIN PENWALLET**, returned from the wider world of *Polytechnica*, to open a shop full of pure & morally wholesome foods:

And bloody expensive it is, too!

Kevin

The Webers are staying with Kevin....

When I first came here, this shop didn't represent a situation of **ONGOING VIABILITY**....

...local **SEA & LAND-DEPENDENT** nutritional customs were eroded by **CAKE MIX** and **FISH FINGERS**.

Through this shop, I'm giving to Tresoddit what **CIVILISATION** has taken away: the **ELEMENTARY STRUCTURES OF NUTRITION**.

Not CHEAP, though, Kevin

Ah, but **NATURE** doesn't **CUT CORNERS**!

At the **Poly**, I was **FED UP** listening to your abstract **SOCIAL PRESCRIPTIONS**...

I prefer **INVOLVED KNOWING** — like talking to old **HAWKINS** there, about his **tomatoes**.

Take old Hawkins — **THERE** you have a man who has never deviated from **ECOLOGICALLY-DIVERSIFIED, ORGANIC HOMESTEADING**....

..a man who's in touch with **NATURE** & its **INTERFACE** with the **SELF**.

Here he is! Hello, Fred!

Marnin' Kevin — I brought my little list, dear

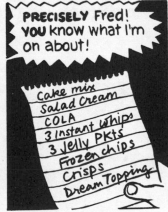

PRECISELY Fred! **YOU** know what I'm on about!

Cake mix
Salad Cream
COLA
3 Instant Whips
3 Jelly Pkts
Frozen chips
Crisps
Dream Topping

You've collated a fine list of the major **BIO-CULTURAL POISONS**!

POISONS?

They're for our Joyce's party.

'hasn't got them as usual, Mary — lucky it's **BUS DAY**!

August

Thursday. Arrived home. Journey O.K. except Benji & Tamsin carsick.
  Had picnic near Exeter — saw lovely hillside, dotted with red & white flowers.
When we got nearer, saw that the flowers were sweet papers, bits of old
Kleenex.
  House seems v. small. Decayed lettuce in frig. drawer. Went to bed early
with Graham Greene.

August

...As for Pippa's birthday teas! I don't know HOW she does it! She's made a cake with bright green butter icing, like a football pitch. The children only eat CRISPS.

Cassandra, don't take one bite out of everything! Finish what's on your plate.

Doesn't ANYONE want any CAKE?

Then the children leave the groaning board, & win MORE prizes. Benji still doesn't join in....

Oh, it's only a book!

No, we're going camping this year.

Hallo Benji!

Mummee!

..Eventually, the parents arrive & put away QUANTITIES of sherry.....

..we say our goodbyes and Benji gets a going-home present.

I'm afraid Benji had a TINY ACCIDENT... his trousers are in this plastic bag & I've given him an old pair of Josh's - don't bother to give them back.

I'm sure Benji's unsociability is a rejection of the nagging MATERIALISM of our society & his private WAR on WANT.

September

Fri. Trish drops in — asks us to party on Sat. to meet J.D. CROUCH (the novelist). Great social coup for Stanhope. Must say, I don't like Crouch's novels — the one about Essex in the Depression... 'Out of Flatley' — wasn't it filmed as 'Timberlust'?

Apparently, CROUCH now rolling in it, living as tax exile in Ireland. For a huge consideration has allowed Stanhope's Agency to shoot commercial for Instant Irish Coffee in his mansion.

September

Saturday. Mummy & Father came for lunch. Showed them holiday photos. Kids showed them their mosquito bites. After tea, Benji sick as a pig — too many plums. Duvet RUINED. Consequently, couldn't go to Stanhope's party. George should have gone on his own, but he disapproves of CROUCH.

Oh God! A teenage literary GROUPIE!

"Maintain eye contact & smile..."

"You've gained an entrée! How do you break the ice?

Easy: just use the ECHO TECHNIQUE of repeating something that has been said.."

So, you're taking my stepmother out to lunch?

"Remember, be an ACTIVE listener...nod & smile at responses.."

Who I lunch with is NONE of your business, young lady.

"Show a sincere interest in the person — remember: he may be SHY too!"

The Art of Charismatic Conversation by

I hear you're writing yet ANOTHER novel about ESSEX during the Depression...

Will it be like "Last Bus from Braintree", or more like your first, "Out of Flatley"?

You must be making POTS of money...how amazing to be a tax exile in IRELAND!

Have you found it easy to forget your SOCIALIST PRINCIPLES now you're a landowner?

I think she's one of the most unpleasant people I've ever met!

"You too can stand out in a crowd. You too can fire a man's blood, you too can be unforgettable."

The Art of Charismatic Conversation by

Stanhope & Trish are entertaining yet again! Jocasta observes the preparations.....

Aren't one's parents' dinner parties EASY, nowadays!

Not that one's parents have DINNER PARTIES as such any more...one just has 'a few people in for a meal,' doesn't one, Dad?..

One doesn't have to IMPRESS people any more – GONE are the days of those ghastly COMPETITIVE meals: 5 pretentious courses, which take ALL day to cook & use up 2 weeks' housekeeping!

And isn't CONSPICUOUS CONSUMPTION rather REVOLTING in these SOMBRE times? Especially as one is entertaining RADICALS & LEFT WING LITERATI, this evening.

People have to take you as they find you, nowadays

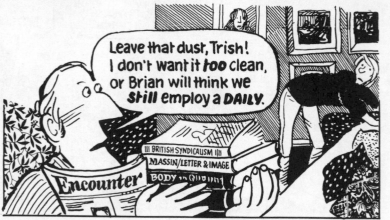

Leave that dust, Trish! I don't want it too clean, or Brian will think we still employ a DAILY.

BRITISH SYNDICALISM

MASSIN/LETTER & IMAGE

Encounter

BODY in QUANT

One just makes the room into a sweet disorder of cushions & important books.

Now, d'you think I've brought in enough BOOKS, Trish? ≶PHEW!≶

Thank God I haven't got to dress up!

Shall I wear a JACKET?

No, a jacket's wrong...

Perhaps a Turnbull & Asser without a tie..

..But Michael always wears a T shirt & donkey jacket...

..& Brian often wears a SUIT... Oh God! Help me Trish....

Encounter

Now, the FOOD couldn't be more simple! ...completely without ostentation... some sprats fried in butter...a spinach quiche or 2...& a few odds & ends whizzed up in the blender, to make a meek soup....

FLOUR

September

American Bald Eagle
Tiger.

Tues   Plan plot for a children's novel.
        Helped Sophie do her project: World map of DESERTIFICATION & ENDANGERED
SPECIES.   S. had further ambitions for map – wanted to add Nuclear Reactor
sites and DANGER ZONES for Plutonium leaks. Am very proud of her.
        George helped on Reactor sites, but was less good on SPECIES – otter, wolf,
whale, peregrine falcon etc. George said GONKS were endangered species
– whatever happened to them? Last one he saw was in my Ma's garage.

weds Cinema Babysitter ✓

Thursday Look after Willy for Trish. She seems to be permanently entertaining
        Stanhope's clients. She should make HIM cook.
        Jocasta apparently looking for a flat – sharing with other students. T. says
thank God, as J. being a right pain at the moment.

October

Friday: Heeps invited us for dinner. George tried to back out as usual, but put my foot down for once & insisted. When we got there, found Trish AND <u>STANHOPE</u>. Don't know how she persuaded him!

I do like to see Jo for old times' sake. She's coaching hockey & lacrosse at St L's this term.

Draw up a **BOLLARD** & sit ye down!

This year, the Xmas pack of **GLEN CRAIOGHDOAN** whisky comes with a free calendar. Edmund's firm has given him one of the original paintings for the calendar, as an incentive bonus.

Look what I got for being a **GOOD BOY**!

Stanhope...**YOU** know how many beans make 5 in the **ART WORLD**...I bet this is worth a **BOB** or 2!

"Even-Gloam: GLEN CRAIOGHDOAN"

Well...if you like that **SORT OF THING**... Frankly, it's not worth the cost of the frame....

EH?

It's just a big, bland **POLAROID**, done with a **PAINT BRUSH**.

Are you **EXTRACTING THE MICHAEL**, Stan? It's a **REAL** painting!

No, it's a very bad rendering of a **TRITE & MAWKISH** subject... not a patch on a **LANDSEER**...

LANCIA?...really? Our District Manager's got a Lancia...very **PRICEY**.....

October

Heep offspring didn't make appearance.
Dinner was CHEESE FONDUE followed by CHOCOLATE FONDUE.
G. bilious in night.

You see, Edmund, we now look for a sense of **SOCIAL PURPOSE** in painting... **NOT** the **RUDE VITALITY** of **GUTTOSO**, nor the *banal* *formalisations* of **LEGER**....

?

But ACTUALLY... now I look at it closer.. in its OWN WAY, it is a GRAPHIC explication of the **GEDDES VALLEY SECTION**...

The **FOLK/WORK/PLACE** dependencies **are** inherently immanent

Come again, George?

As the actress said!

..but using the interaction of the **PLASTIC** configurations on the canvas to...to...

..to **HINT** at the changing **WORKER-MANAGEMENT RELATIONSHIPS!**

Yes, George...it may be an aesthetic experience of a **LOW** order...but it does show **BRAND IMAGE** taken to a fine art...

I wish my **CREATIVE DEPT.** could come up with a **MARKETING** idea in this class.

It's a piece of contemporary cultural **ARCHAEOLOGY**.....

THOUGHT SO! ...worth a bit, after all, eh George? Well, I'll flog it...

Here's looking up your **KILT**, Squire!

Glen Craioghdoan HIGHLAND MALT WHISKY

October

Weds. George's late lecture.

Belinda at home with chill. Not surprised—she's always necking outside the front door in the freezing cold with that boy. Why don't they do it in the house? Belinda's got a perfectly good room. It's so FURTIVE & it looks so awful for the neighbours — They'll think George & I disapprove. Wish B. would get an INTEREST — like Jocasta or those HEEP boys. She just slouches round the house, pitting

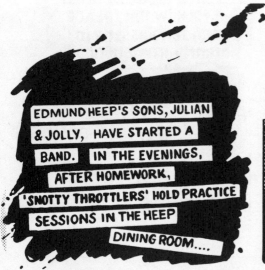

EDMUND HEEP'S SONS, JULIAN & JOLLY, HAVE STARTED A BAND. IN THE EVENINGS, AFTER HOMEWORK, 'SNOTTY THROTTLERS' HOLD PRACTICE SESSIONS IN THE HEEP DINING ROOM....

I'm a sexual Band-it, usin' my body as a hide-out.... Coppin' out, can't wait to join the Dole queue...

That's no ******* use, Julian, you ☆9!☆, you got to ☆☆☆☆☆*** make it sound more ****☆☆☆ BORING! O.K!

C'mon then... let's do the next bit, Jolly, about your Dad...

My Dad's a suburban moron, wiv a small mind....

...Rates an' mortgage an' a company car—God, I hates that Vehicle! I got Mal de Siècle!

October

the cork tiles with those frightful heels.

October

Friday: Shan't say anything but DO think Belinda's bloke is a bit much — effs & blinds & treats B. like an object. Awful thing is, B. doesn't seem to mind. So much for liberation.

Wonder what his parents think of him — though, as old Moorish proverb says 'EVERY BEETLE is a gazelle in the eyes of its mother'.

Belinda Weber has got a new boyfriend... Jasper....

Those trousers are a bit MUCH, Belinda!

Yeah... nice behind, eh? Like 2 hard boiled eggs in a handkerchief....

That's an extremely CRUDE & SEXIST remark, Jasper.

But, on the other hand, Belinda DOES invite it... dressed up like a *fille de joie*....

Belinda's not into EQUALITY.. she's into PASSION. She's not into COSY companionship between EQUALS... she's into MACHISMO and VIOLENCE.

Really? I wonder what BELINDA thinks... she's got a MIND, you know...

But, on the other hand, ...I suppose FASHION is free speech....

"But on the other hand"! That's a typical remark of you woolly liberals! LOOK at YOU!

October

Oct 20th Autumn Fayre / Assembly Rms.   (Chutney?)

Father's Birthday
= card.

November

Tuesday. George rather solemn. After supper said he had something important
    to tell me in private. We sit in the kitchen.
George says he has finally made an appointment to have a VASECTOMY.
    After 4 years of thinking it over.

I am flabbergasted. But very pleased. GOODBYE COIL. I never thought he'd
come round to it & didn't want to pressure him.
Suppose G. always felt more defensive than me about having
so many children. <u>I</u> think people should be free to have several,
    few or none at all.

G. still looked solemn - perhaps worried about the op? Then he said
he had an awful row at the Poly today. That bloody man Pratt
has cut George's lectures on "Language as Discourse"!

736702
Caroline
Anna.

Saturday   FIRE-WORK PARTY

Lentil soup
spuds in foil

Soak kidney beans, mung beans
black eye beans.
Not too much chili powder

✓ Pickles
✓ Chutney
✓ Ketchup
✓ Rolls
✓ French Bread } freezer
✓ Bangers

Sparklers
Milk bottles
Matches

Sophie → Warn old dears about BANGS
Ben →   " street shut their pets up.

Tamsin Weber

December

George's Ma rings up about Xmas. Are we going there this year? Heart sinks — remember last year — 4 days of George defending the Unions & comprehensives & Anthea defending Mr SMITH... yes, and the kids all had colds & we had a burst pipe when we got back. I play for time. Anyway, I DID promise Sara N. I'd join in her scheme of driving O.A.P.s to their families over Christmas.

George has to give a speech of thanks & a cheque to the canteen lady, who's

"As one of the longer-serving lecturers here at the POLY...."

"...it is my great pleasure to remind the Staff & students that, after 15 years' service, **Marie** is going to New Zealand.... and, therefore, things in the canteen can only get **better**..."

"I think one can say that, during **Marie's** despotic reign, **never** in the field of institutional cooking has so **much** food been left by so **many**...."

"I, for one, will not miss her air of **truculence**, her fault finding, her inability to give the right change...."

"I won't miss her **rudeness, her racism,** her petty economies & above all, her **congealing** food, cooked & served in PURE BILE!"

Go on! Take it! What d'you think I am?!

December

retiring — 15 years of loyal service. G. spent most of weekend mouthing in front of bathroom mirror.

Ring Sara

Must empty lint bag in tumble drier

December

Monday: I feel DREADFUL - was in newsagents with Sara N. discussing which of the local elderly
might need a lift or some help over Christmas — I think we might have
referred to them as 'old dears'. Old Mrs Newby was in shop & obviously overheard.
When I asked her if we could help, she said "I'm sure actions speak louder than words,
Mrs Weber, but SOME of your words are bloody patronising!" Felt quite AWFUL. Apologised.

George asked me what I wanted for Xmas. Last year he gave me a steam iron. V. useful, of course.
Said I'd like something frivolous this year.

Now, this is called **SEXPOSÉ** – a ve-ry **NATURAL** look with 3 way convertible straps....

...and this is the look of **TOTAL NUDITY** in satinette... very **NATURAL**....

And this gives a fabulous **separation**.

..and this gives a lovely **DEEP PLUNGE**....

It's **SO UNPLEASANT** how women's bodies are **DISTORTED** to fit an inherently **SYNTHETIC STEREOTYPE!**

Well, what about something else? This **GRECIAN SLAVE** love gown...it also comes in **PIXIE PINK ACETATE**...

Or this saucy **BOUDOIR APRON**?

NO! NO! NO!

I will **NOT** have **MY** wife dressed up as a **SLAVE** in bed...or as a **SEXUAL SKIVVY** in an apron!.....**SEX** as domestic chore..**BLOODY HECK!**

I **WANT** something **PLAIN...NATURAL!** What about these? Have you got these in **BLACK?**

No, only **PEACH**.

I'll take 3 pairs.

They're a very good **QUALITY** cotton..... but they're **HARDLY** a **CHRISTMAS** present, are they?

I mean! **MY WIFE** hasn't got a high **ANXIETY QUOTIENT** about her sexuality...**SHE** doesn't need all that **INSULTING** paraphernalia....

...and all this transparent sexual **SEMIOLOGY**..... I mean... **I** don't snigger at **ROAD SIGNS!**

... but I suppose the **SYNTAGMATIC ORDER** of bra, suspender belt & knickers, could be understood as the **FOUNDATIONS OF STRUCTURALISM**....Ha Ha!

merry Xmas · · merry Xmas

December

tin foil   crackers:
mince meat?   sellotape.
froz. pastry? gift tags.

TV Times
Radio "

untangle Xmas Tree lights

GIN

Monday: Twins chirp up at breakfast: could I make them ANGEL costumes
        ready for school Nativity play on Weds? First I've heard of it.
   Thought that Amanda was NOISES OFF (she's marvellous at sheep) —
 & Tamsin was banging tambourine.
        Apparently 2 angels down with flu.

 Mrs Gilchrist sends note later: could twins have white ballet shoes?
 Spend afternoon putting BLANCO on their pink ones. Make haloes with
 tin foil & wings out of old net curtain.

 While I'm busy, Benji opens ALL the windows on the twins'
 Advent Calendar, including Dec 25th — HELL to pay when
 they got in from school.

   Is it all worth it, I ask myself?

First published 1979
Reprinted 1979 (twice), 1980 (twice), 1982
Copyright © 1979 by Posy Simmonds
Jonathan Cape Ltd, 30 Bedford Square, London WC1

British Library Cataloguing in Publication Data
Simmonds, Posy
Mrs Weber's Diary.
I. Title
741.5'942   NC1479.S/
ISBN 0-224-01719-5

The drawings in this book have been adapted
from episodes of *The Silent Three*, a weekly cartoon
strip appearing in the *Guardian*.

Printed in Great Britain by St Edmundsbury Press Ltd
Bury St Edmunds, Suffolk